Edition Schott

T0103101

Samuel Coleridge-Taylor
1875–1912

Three Humoresques
Drei Humoresken

for Piano
für Klavier

opus 31

ED 23705
ISMN 979-0-001-21786-6

www.schott-music.com

Mainz · London · Madrid · Paris · New York · Tokyo · Beijing
© 2023 Schott Music GmbH & Co. KG, Mainz · Printed in Germany

Preface

Samuel Coleridge-Taylor's *Three Humoresques* for solo piano were first published in 1898 by Augener Ltd. Following George Augener's retirement in 1910, the work along with the whole Augener catalogue (which contained no less than 24 other works by Coleridge-Taylor), was acquired by Schott & Co. Ltd. At this time both companies occupied offices on Great Marlborough Street, London.

Coleridge-Taylor was born in London and brought up in Croydon. He learnt to play the violin, was recognized as a child prodigy and at 15 was awarded a scholarship to study at the Royal College of Music with Charles Villiers Stanford, where he was a contemporary of Gustav Holst and Vaughan Williams.

Coleridge-Taylor described himself Anglo-African and, despite support from his colleagues, faced racism throughout his whole career. In spite of this prejudice and his tragically early death in 1912 aged just 37, he enjoyed great success during his lifetime and his music was performed at the Proms no less than 116 times between 1898 and 1939. In contrast, since 1940 his music has only been heard there on eleven occasions to date.

Like many works, at some point in the past *Three Humoresques* became out of print. Schott Music is now very pleased to present this new modern performing edition with errors and inconsistencies from the original edition now corrected.

Vorwort

Samuel Coleridge-Taylors *Three Humoresques* für Klavier solo wurden 1898 erstmals von Augener Ltd. veröffentlicht. Nachdem sich George Augener 1910 aus dem Geschäftsleben zurückzog, wurde das Werk zusammen mit dem gesamten Augener-Katalog (der nicht weniger als 24 andere Werke Coleridge-Taylors enthielt) von Schott & Co. Ltd erworben. Beide Unternehmen hatten zu dieser Zeit Niederlassungen in der Great Marlborough Street in London.

Coleridge-Taylor wurde in London geboren und wuchs in Croydon auf. Er erlernte das Geigenspiel, wurde als Wunderkind anerkannt und erhielt als Fünfzehnjähriger ein Stipendium für ein Studium am Royal College of Music bei Charles Villiers Stanford, wo er ein Zeitgenosse von Gustav Holst und Vaughan Williams war.

Coleridge-Taylor bezeichnete sich selbst als anglo-afrikanisch und war trotz der Unterstützung seiner Kollegen während seiner gesamten Karriere mit Rassismus konfrontiert. Trotz vieler Vorurteile und einer tragisch kurzen Lebensspanne – er starb bereits 1912 im Alter von nur 37 Jahren – feierte er zu Lebzeiten große Erfolge und seine Musik wurde zwischen 1898 und 1939 sogar 116 mal bei den *Proms* aufgeführt. Seit 1940 hingegen waren seine Kompositionen dort nur noch elfmal zu hören.

Wie viele Werke waren auch die *Three Humoresques* irgendwann in Vergessenheit geraten und schließlich vergriffen. Schott Music freut sich nun sehr, diese revidierte und korrigierte Neuauflage präsentieren zu dürfen.

Content / Inhalt

Three Humoresques
Drei Humoresken
op. 31

Samuel Coleridge-Taylor
1875—1912

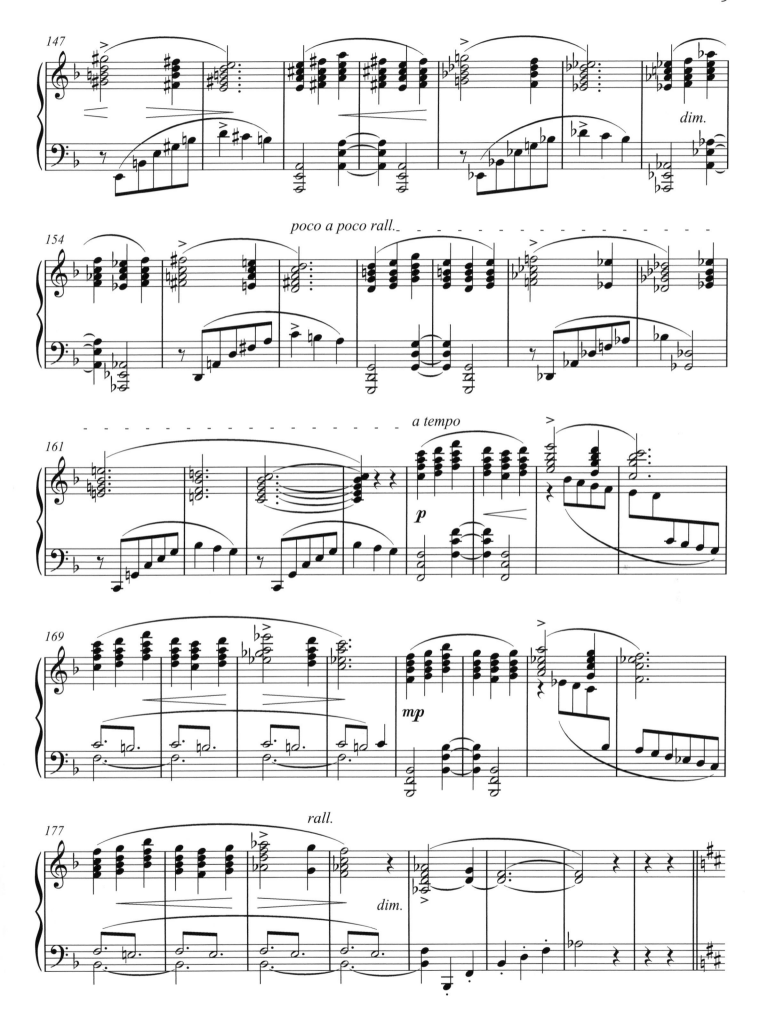

Molto vivace

2

3

D. C. al Fine